THE Home Builders

Written by
VARSHA BAJAJ

Illustrated by
SIMONA MULAZZANI

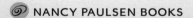 NANCY PAULSEN BOOKS

Do you see the home builders?
Deep on the trail,
Beneath the mound,
Down by the water,
Safe off the ground.

Under the earth,
Below the bridge,
In the tall grass,
High on the ridge.

Do you see the builders work?
Burrow and hide,
Tunnel and creep,

Nibble and gnaw,
Explore and keep.

Shovel and plow,
Construct and flit,

Rummage and roam,
Gather and knit.

Do you see the homes?
Beds in leaf piles,
Dens snug and warm,

Lodges on ponds,
Shelter from storms.

Burrows with rooms,
Beehives and nests,
Each of these homes
Soon will be blessed.

Do you see the babies?
Hatchlings go forth,
Fox cubs nuzzle,

Beaver kits swim,
Owlets huddle.

Mole pups slumber,
Bees swarm the air,

Timid fawns bond,
Wee eaglets stare.

Do you see the families?
Born to be wild,
To work and play,
Learning to soar,
Growing each day.